Date Due

Demco 3o-

RHYTHMS TO READING
Book and Record Sets
A Multi-Sensory Approach to Music and Reading

A companion recording is available for this book and all others in the RHYTHMS TO READING series. Each picture in this book represents an action song or a descriptive musical composition which is included on the long-playing record.

The simple text under each picture provides a unique, multi-sensory experience for the young child. He reads about the activities to which he has just responded in movement and song. This text is also included on the recording for classroom use or at the listening post.

On the left-hand page, beginning on page 4, are printed the full story and song lyrics heard on the recording. This page is for the use of teachers, parents and children who have had reading experience.

Repetition is essential to learning. Learning which might otherwise be derived from tedious drill is here developed in an enjoyable, esthetic context.

Research indicates that children learn to read more quickly and easily words that are related to large muscle activity, esthetic experience and tongue-tickling rhymes.

When reading experiences are introduced through music, song and vigorous movement

- *memory is reinforced and tensions released, creating an atmosphere that encourages learning.*
- *the flow of language comes more naturally, encouraging the child to read in complete sentences.*
- *the number of clues which aid the child in reading are multiplied.*
- *word meanings are clarified and sight vocabulary is developed automatically.*

Copyright © 1971 by Bowmar Publishing Corp. All rights reserved including the right to reproduce this book or parts thereof in any form. Library of Congress Catalog Card No. 71-139702. Printed in the United States of America. International copyright secured.

We made a little tugboat, Timothy Twilliger Tug.

We made a little tugboat.
His name is Timothy Twilliger Tug.
He lives in our make-believe harbor
and pushes and pulls the big ships.
We go chugging along over the water
with Timothy Twilliger Tug.

Chug-a-long, chug-a-long, chug, chug, chug
Out in the harbor, little red tug;
Chug-a-long, chug-a-long, choo, choo, choo,
We can chug-a-long just like you.

We sail around the harbor on Timothy Twilliger Tug.

In our harbor there are bell buoys
with a red light and bell that guide the ships.
How would it feel to be a bell buoy
with the water moving under you,
lifting you up and dropping you down?
Let's be bell buoys rocking on the waves.

Little bell buoy rocking, a-rocking, a-rocking,
Little bell buoy rocking, a-rocking all day.
Back and forth and up and down,
Back and forth and up and down.

Little bell buoy ringing, a-ringing, a-ringing,
Little bell buoy ringing, a-ringing all day.
Ding-dong, ding-dong, ding-dong, ding;
Ding-dong, ding-dong, ding-dong, ding.

We rock like the bell buoys. Ding-dong-ding! Ding-dong-ding!

We go chugging along over the water
to see the lighthouse on the shore.

Chug-a-long, chug-a-long, chug, chug, chug
Out in the harbor, little red tug;
Chug-a-long, chug-a-long, choo, choo, choo,
We can chug-a-long just like you.

We sail with Timothy Twilliger Tug to see the lighthouse.

We turn around and around
like the light on the lighthouse.
Our arms reach out like the light
that goes out over the water
to warn the ships away from the rocks.

Round and round I'm turning,
Round and round I'm turning,
Round and round I'm turning,
Sending out my light.

Round and round I'm turning,
Round and round I'm turning,
Round and round I'm turning,
Guiding ships at night.

We turn around like the light in the lighthouse, round and round.

Timothy Twilliger Tug
takes us way out in the ocean.

Chug-a-long, chug-a-long, chug, chug, chug
Out in the harbor, little red tug;
Chug-a-long, chug-a-long, choo, choo, choo,
We can chug-a-long just like you.

We sail out into the ocean.

We sing as we sail along over the water.

Hey-ho, we'll all go sailing,
Hey-ho, we'll all go sailing,
Hey-ho, we'll all go sailing,
Early in the morning.

One little, two little, three little sailors,
Four little, five little, six little sailors,
Seven little, eight little, nine little sailors,
Early in the morning.
(Repeat)

We sing a sailor's song. Hey-ho! Hey-ho!

Out on the ocean
we fish with our fishing poles and lines.

I throw my line way out in the ocean,
I throw my line way out in the sea,
I throw my line way out in the ocean,
And wait, wait, wait.

I catch a fish, pull it in from the ocean,
I catch a fish, pull it in from the sea,
I catch a fish, pull it in from the ocean,
And pull, pull, pull.
(Repeat)

We catch fish in the ocean, one, two, three.

We go chugging along, back over the water
to a sandy beach.

Chug-a-long, chug-a-long, chug, chug, chug
Out in the harbor, little red tug;
Chug-a-long, chug-a-long, choo, choo, choo,
We can chug-a-long just like you.

Sometimes we let Timothy Twilliger Tug rest
while we sit on the beach and watch the waves.
Little waves rush up to us and tickle our toes.
The little waves are soft and gentle
like a puppy dog's tongue.
Splash, splash, splash.

We sit on the beach and let the little waves tickle our toes.

Then all of a sudden, a big wave comes.
The big wave is like a huge monster chasing us
and we run, run, run, faster and faster
across the sand.
Then we turn and chase the big wave
as it rolls back out to the ocean
because it isn't really a big monster
and it can't scare us!

We run, run, run from the monster waves.

Suddenly, many sea horses come galloping, galloping out of the water. We gallop with them. High into the air we leap
as we gallop over the sand and water.

We gallop over the water like sea horses.

Little sea gulls walk in the sand and water.
We watch them and play a sea gull game song.

Little gray sea gulls sitting on the sand,
Chirping and talking on a sunny day,
Big mother sea gull says, "Go find your lunch,"
And all the little sea gulls fly away.

The little gray sea gulls fly through the sky,
Up and around and around,
They see a fish in the water below,
And fly down, down, down.
(Repeat)

We fly and dive like the sea gulls. Down! Down! Down!

Then Timothy Twilliger Tug
takes us back into the harbor again.

Chug-a-long, chug-a-long, chug, chug, chug
Out in the harbor, little red tug;
Chug-a-long, chug-a-long, choo, choo, choo,
We can chug-a-long just like you.

We sail back into the harbor on Timothy Twilliger Tug.

In the harbor we see many kinds of boats.
We pretend that we are in a rowboat.
Sometimes we like to lie down
and let the boat rock us.

I sit in my boat and row and row,
Row and row all day;
I sit in my boat and row and row,
Row far away.

We row and row all day.

I lie in my boat and rock and rock
Out on the ocean deep;
I lie in my boat till the stars come out
And soon I fall asleep.

We rock in the boat and fall asleep.